# SONGS OF STARLIGHT

## Brian Andreas

W0007647

flying edna

ISBN 978-0-9981490-1-1
Copyright ©2019 by Flying Edna LLC

All rights are reserved. No part of this book may be repro-
duced or transmitted in any form, or by any means, electronic
or mechanical, including photocopying, recording, or by any
information storage and retrieval system, without permission
in writing from the Publisher.

FLYING EDNA
PO Box 7088
Bozeman, MT 59771
flyingedna.com

YAY! ANOTHER PLANET-FRIENDLY
KEEPSAKE FROM FLYING EDNA.

Printed by Hemlock (a FSC-certified carbon
neutral printing company based in Seattle,
Washington, USA & Vancouver, BC, Canada)
Interior pages: 100% post consumer waste
Exterior: FSC certified. Green Seal certified

First Edition: September 15, 2019
Printed in Canada

*This book you hold in your hands is the result of many conversations. With the everyday moments. With the places I live. With the people I know who see clearly & speak true.*

*I am grateful beyond what I can say for two of those clear-sighted people who went beyond conversation to helping shape the actual book.*

*To Cris Hamilton. My friend. My fierce champion & luckiest of all for me, my sister.*

*To Fia Skye. My equally fierce love. For your laughter & delight in our days. For your love of stones & wood & wild things & especially for the way you choose an us that's as big as the Montana sky.*

*Thank you both for your generosity & love & your insistence on what this really wanted to be.*

*& finally to all of you who choose every day to imagine a world that holds us all, no exceptions...*

Other books by Brian Andreas:

*Mostly True*
*Still Mostly True*
*Going Somewhere Soon*
*Strange Dreams*
*Hearing Voices*
*Story People*
*Trusting Soul*
*Traveling Light*
*Some Kind of Ride*
*Peculiar Times (e-book)*
*Theories of Everything*
*Something Like Magic*
*Impossible to Know*
*Bring Your Life Back to Life*

With Fia Skye:
*Creative Anarchy*

With Lorne Resnick:
*Cuba: This Moment Exactly So*

# first things...

None of this you need you know. Because you already know it. It is only gathered here in one place as a reminder for those times you forget.

Because you will forget & remember & forget & remember, over & over again.

Whether you are one who walks with bare feet on the earth & loves things done carefully by hand. Or one who hears the way the high crystal songs of the crickets call down the heat lightning in the thick summer. Or one who moves lightly through the world, like the shadow of fast moving clouds.

No matter what sits at the heart of you, never forget that who you are is an act of imagination.

It is easy to forget that as you go through your days. That you are made to hold infinities. Of the world. Of the stars. Of each other.

With love,

15 August 2019

I want to do something that
is filled with light for us all &
it turns out the easiest way to
start is just saying I love you
& I'm glad you're here.

You are made of
the same stardust
as all creation.

Why would
you believe that
something so
marvelous as
that can't be
trusted to
know how
to live?

You will do your
best seeing when
you're not looking
so hard for what
you think you
should find.

My favorite time
is in the beginning
when I'm still quiet
enough to hear
a whole new world
showing up.

I used to think everything
had a deeper meaning, but
as I go on, it's more like Oh,
that's an interesting thing
I could easily mistake for
something that means
something.

Just because there's a rule for
something doesn't mean that's
the only way to do it. It just
means that if your way doesn't
work, a lot of the people you know
who follow all the rules will be
more smug than usual.

## THREE THINGS TO KNOW ABOUT YOUR RIGHT PATH:

1. If you're on the right path, you know it bone deep.

2. On days you can't tell if you're on the right path, you are, but you can't see it because you're thinking it should look like a different path.

3. If you think you're on the wrong path, you're not. Because there is no wrong path. There are only paths that go places you weren't expecting.

Bonus thing: Every path you take is one step at a time. If it feels wrong, take a different step & then another one until it feels right.

(This is not an exact science.)

Just so you know, finding your path is always easier once you choose where you want to go.

What is it called when you think
you move through the world
gracefully & you still wake up
every morning & find new bruises
where you bumped into things?

(I'm currently calling it
Gracing The Shit Out Of
Things. Until I come up
with a better name.)

My aunt told me once there were only two real questions I'd have to answer: how can I help? & what excuses do I have not to?

I laughed & said I was sure I'd have more than two & she smiled & said, That's what happens when you don't answer the real questions & then she looked at me, still & soft & she said, I expect more of you, though.

It took me until now to see how, in that moment, she gave me my whole life.

In my dream, I told the angel I was tired of being nudged towards my best self all the time & she started laughing.

Then, she put her hand on my arm.

You already are your best self, she said. I just show up now & then because I'm curious to see if you remember.

Trust your instincts to go towards joy.

(Also, trust your instincts to stay away from people who tell you your instincts are wrong.)

Someone told her today you need the dark to
appreciate the light & for a moment, she tried
to believe it was true. But then she snapped
out of it & decided to hell with that & went off
& appreciated the light all on its own.

Things I'm absolutely
certain about today:

1. chocolate in reasonable
quantities is never a bad
thing. (I can't be certain
though if what you call
reasonable is the same as
what I call reasonable)

2. Nothing else yet.

When I was younger, I always
wanted to have superpowers &
it took me until now to see I got
the best one of all: waking up
every day constantly amazed
at being alive.

this is a special compass
guaranteed to show you
the quickest way towards
your true north & you'd
be surprised how many
people return it & say it's
broken because it keeps
pointing in different
directions than they
expect (because, after
all, heading north first
isn't always how you
get there).

I'm not so much cleaning, she said, as I'm re-arranging.

What's the difference? I said.

If I was cleaning, I'd have to throw a lot of it out.

There are no impossible things, he said. Only things that aren't possible from your point of view & it took me a long time to grow up enough to hear that.

Just be yourself, she said, with maybe one or two filters & you'll be fine (& I almost snorted coffee out of my nose)

In my dream, the angel said, you can only know something so long before you have to admit it to yourself

& I said I haven't found any real time limit myself & she laughed so loud I woke up & from far away, I heard her say, Time's up.

I've always been better at the future. Because my present got booked up months ago.

There's no rule anywhere here for what to do now. There are only suggestions for where to listen if you're having a hard time hearing.

In my dream, everyone was racing around at three times normal speed, while I went around quietly touching things, like a book laying there forgotten, or the tile of the kitchen counter. Every time I touched something, I heard a voice inside say, Love the things you love.

I looked up & saw you there, touching the world the same way & I could see you heard it, too. Right then, your eyes met mine & something inside me sang low & true.

Suddenly, none of the other people rushing about mattered. Because there we were, holding hands & you smiled at me & we turned into the day & went off to love what we loved together.

Tell me again why you think you need to work so hard all the time when the times you're most alive are barely any effort at all.

You can accomplish
an enormous amount
of wrong things while
you're being right.

On the day you open your heart to a
dog, don't be surprised when the whole
rest of the world starts to fit in there,
too.

So much depends on
paying attention when
the people right in front
of you are trying their
best to love.

I want to learn magic, I said. Where do I start?
My grandfather looked up from the book he was
reading. Stop learning all the stuff that's not
magic, he said. It'll be easier than having to
forget it all later.

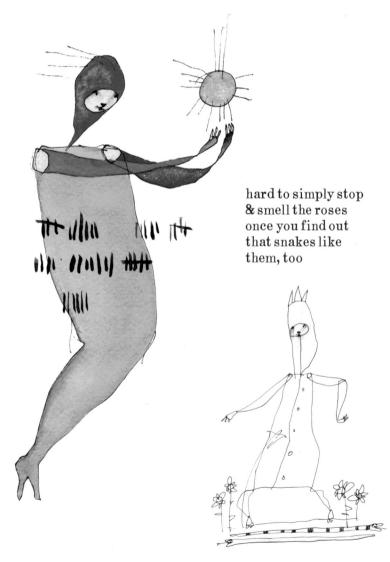

hard to simply stop
& smell the roses
once you find out
that snakes like
them, too

All you need to do to HAVE a
MaGiCAL LiFe ★★

with No filler whAtSoever So it'll Be
Really eASy to ReMemBer. oK?

#1. StoP HidiNG.

#2. Seriously. stop HidinG. no
more lies. no more SecretS. No
more Being Addicted to what
people tHiNK. (WARNING!!
Do hot read #3 until After you
do this. Even though you & I Both
know you will. But it Won't do you
Any good. Oh well. go AheaD.)

#3. You NeVer Aren't in a Magical
LiFe. So. yeah. Now go Back
& stArt with #1.

this is her signature move where she leaps
into the world with no idea how she'll land

> (& her other signature move is
> immediately looking back &
> thinking, What have I done?)

Her favorite thing about flying is just flying.
Her second favorite thing is ignoring all the
people she knows who tell her it's not possible.

From the very first, you knew
she was someone you'd like to be
someday. Someone whose joy
says to everyone she meets, Oh my.
Aren't you an astonishing thing.

For a long time, I thought I was lucky to
have fierce women who walked beside me
& now I see the real luck was that these fierce
women stayed there until I figured out how
to be fierce myself.

for the longest time, I thought the
big stuff was more important than
the little stuff. But it turns out the
little stuff is all of it & the big stuff
is mainly what makes us miss that.

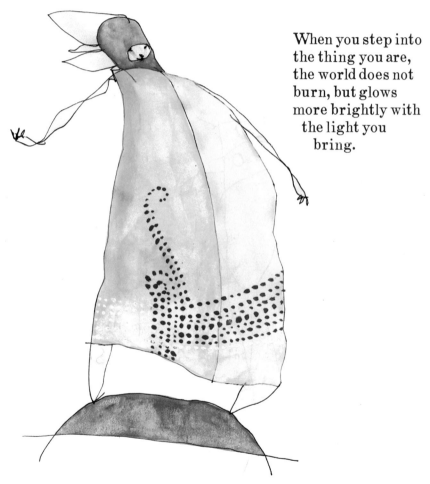

When you step into
the thing you are,
the world does not
burn, but glows
more brightly with
the light you
bring.

making peace today with the fact that I'm never going
to be one of those people who leaves things undersaid

# tHings i do to Get started

1. Wait until the exact moment when everything aligns perfectly, so it comes together naturally, like breathing.

2. After awhile of doing that, I usually hear my grandmother say something like, For crying out loud, kid, those beans aren't going to weed themselves.

3. Since my grandmother died twenty years ago, this is about the only time we talk, but that's usually all it takes to get me started.

Gathering the day
into her arms &
even if it spills
out a little at
the edges, still,
she wants it
all to know
it's loved.

the first rule is never
believe the story you
tell about you. it is like
a cage around a wild
thing & why would you
believe that a spirit
so large would ever
choose to say, Who
I am is this cage.

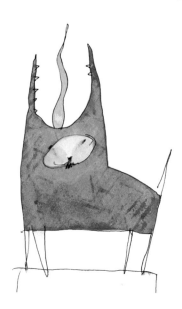

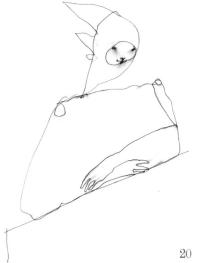

her favorite thing
about fences is
leaning on them
& talking with
whoever happens
to be on the other
side

One time picking strawberries
with my grandmother, she held
one out to me.

Taste it, she said. & I took a bite
& she said, Stop. Close your eyes.
Now, taste it all again.

It was sun-warm & sweet
& there was the sound of
bees & the feel of the earth,
hot beneath my toes

& I opened my eyes &
she smiled & said,
Nothing finer.

Even now, I remember
what it is to taste
it all like that.

I will always remember the way you'd laugh
& clap your hands watching us play & then
later, before bed, you'd gather us in your
arms & whisper, Have you ever seen
a world so perfect?

filled with big thoughts in
the early morning before
the rest of the world wakes
up & brings her back to
a more manageable size.

It's funny how little it matters if
I agree with life because I don't
really know a thing about what it
plans to do next anyway.

Now & then, I'll be walking down the street & I'll see someone glow with light & I'll say a quick prayer of gratitude for that reminder that it's everywhere all the time, but I've gotten too distracted to see it for awhile

& I vow not to forget, but after awhile, I do. Until the next time it happens & I wonder if that's how it works, that we light up now & then to say to each other This is who you are.

interpretive
sunrise dance
with maybe a smidge
of personal drama
thrown in there
for artistic effect

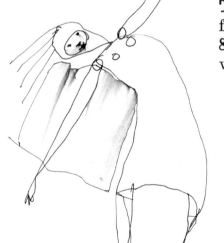

There is room enough
for all of us in this world
& room enough for exactly
who you want to be.

It doesn't take much really,
she said. Mainly you just
have to hear the music
that's already there.

There is nothing I can say
that will bring them back,
all of their bright futures
spread before us. But I
will stand here all the
same with you, my heart
broken open with yours
& remember what
we have lost.

In my dream, I was having a beer with Death
& we talked about everything under the sun &
the thing that struck me most was how easily
Death laughed & cried at the smallest of
things & I remember thinking, this is one of
the most alive people I've ever met.

Because Death does not take things lightly,
the running your fingers like a prayer over
every bit of the world, saying quietly with
each breath, thank you for this chance to love.

Someone asked me
yesterday how to live
an extraordinary life
& I said I had no idea,

because
I always
found it's more
interesting to live
an ordinary life
& not miss
a second
of it.

Once when I was young, I went on a trip with my grandfather. Now & then we'd speak, but mainly we drove for miles in silence.

Just at dusk, he spoke, still looking straight ahead. Remember this, he said, knowing something & talking about it are two different things. I nodded & we rode on quietly into the evening & now, all these years later, I'm ready to turn to him & say, I know what you mean.

finally starting to
see that the life she
always imagined
isn't anywhere near
the life that wants
to imagine her

Most people know this if they stop to think
about it: anyone can talk to the wind.

It's as simple as saying something like,
Hey, Wind. Or How's it going?

Most people don't do this because they think
they'll look crazy.

Which they do, if they hang out with the
kind of people who don't hear the wind
when it answers.

once you begin to see the heroes around you,
the ones that stand quietly & love the world
with everything they are, it is hard to miss
that you are bigger because of them & don't
be surprised if one day you choose to stand
up, too & show what happens when you
live that kind of life.

It is like a perfect golden sunrise, that
moment when your whole self wakes &
everything that came before feels like
dreaming of your real life.

Who can say why they started seeing magic in the most unexpected places? But it took them barely any time at all to understand it happened entirely because it was the two of them together.

IN case i've Somehow FoRgotten to tell you, i'D do it ALL OVER again in a HeArtbeat.

The other day I brought home a bag of apples because she was baking a pie & when I set them down she said, How many are there?

All of a sudden, I wondered if numbers ever wished they could get out & live a little without everyone expecting them to be the same all the time. So, I started with seven & then twenty-nine & then six, because I have a soft spot for sixes.

She said, What did you come up with? & I said the next number that came to mind. Which was fifty-one. She counted & said, There are twelve. I said, That's a good number, too & I will use it next time I have to count something. She smiled & kissed me & said, Just so you know, I almost picked fifty-one, too.

Every day. Every single day, I offer a prayer of thanks that there's an entire world to discover with you by my side.

Not quite sure
it matters where
the art of cooking ends
& the art of eating begins

bringing magic back
into everyday life,
even though to most
people, it just looks
like soup.

I had a dream I was in ancient Egypt & all of the
restaurants had weird food that tasted a bit like
mud. But finally, I found a place that had Texas
BBQ, so I got a menu & opened it up. It was all in
hieroglyphics, so I just pointed at something.
The waiter said, That is a very good choice, sir.
Unfortunately, we're all out of it for another 4000
years. Right then, I woke up & went downstairs &
had a snack of leftover BBQ & thought how lucky
I was that it was 4000 years later.

# THREE THINGS YOU NEED TO KNOW ABOUT LIFE...

1. What you know now isn't what you'll know later.

& then 2 other things you'll figure out all on your own.

Inviting all the new things out into the sunlight & the spring air

& even though she knows they were all going to do it anyway, it never hurts to have a friend there waiting for you.

Those stairs don't go
anywhere, he said &
she laughed & said,
It's a beautiful day
& I'm holding your
hand & what on earth
makes you think that
going somewhere
is the point?

there are no beginnings & no
endings. there are only moments
we pay closer attention to the
different directions we go.

reminded again tonight that
we're completely surrounded
by stars in space no matter
how often we just stare at
the ground wondering
where the magic
has gone.

that moment when
the life you imagined
meets the life you'll
discover, now you're
walking side by side
with it.

In the beginning, you learn the words for
things & you think you somehow know all
about them since you have their names held
tight in your hand.

Later, there is a more important lesson you
learn. That words are ever only a memory of
the thing itself.

Like catching sunlight in your cupped hands
so you have it later when
the dark comes on.

   Sometimes, the words &
   the memory of light are all
   you have to keep you steady
   until the night ends.

# WHY i woNder about LOVe

SomeOne asked me the other day WHY I WoNder so much about LOVe. It is like breathing, she said, a THing we just do Naturally & I said Yes & like BREATHING, even though We do it, We do Not ALL do it WELL. We do Not breAthe Deep & true in a way that feeds our Bodies & HEArts & LiVes & I could see her stArt to Breathe More deeply & then she smiled & said, I can see How that is something WORTH WONDeriNg ABout.

this is an angel improvising
something on an untuned
piano & it'd probably be
more impressive if you
didn't know that's
exactly what angels
do most of the time

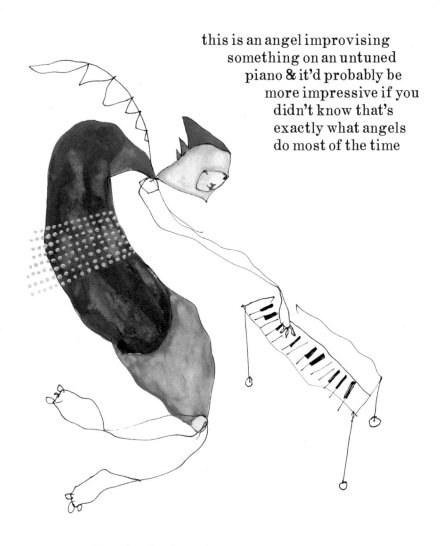

I'm declaring tomorrow a
holiday, he said. What's the
occasion? I said. It's the day
after today & I don't think it
needs any more explanation
than that.

The stories that find you in
the world aren't accidental.

They're saying
Pay attention to
this. This is who
you want to
be next.

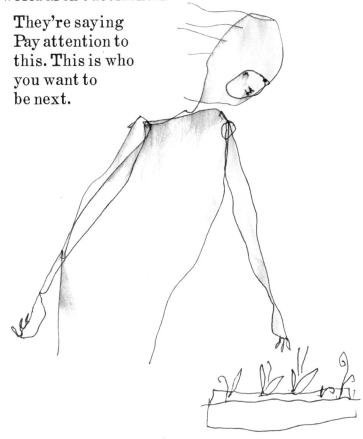

She held her whole life up to the light & it
struck her how beautiful it was, even with
the threads of dark woven through it

& if she cried easily after that it was only
because at last she understood this is
what she is making with the life she got.

There are never any words that
seem enough when you lose a
somebody. No words bring back the
way she laughed. Or the sound of her
voice. Or the way sometimes you'd
catch her looking at you like she was
thinking, Look at you so big & all.

There are no words that
say all that. That say she
was my mother & I will
carry her with me all
the days of my life.

Trust yourself to know
the moment where nothing
else matters but holding life
gratefully in your hands.

One time, I stood with my grandfather at
the edge of a field of strawberries &
sweet corn. The whole world is a garden,
he said & it grows whatever you water
& sometimes lately, I think he would
not be at all surprised to see
what has grown in me from
the places he watered.

It can take awhile to see how many
others walked before you to help
you see this path now that's yours
to walk.

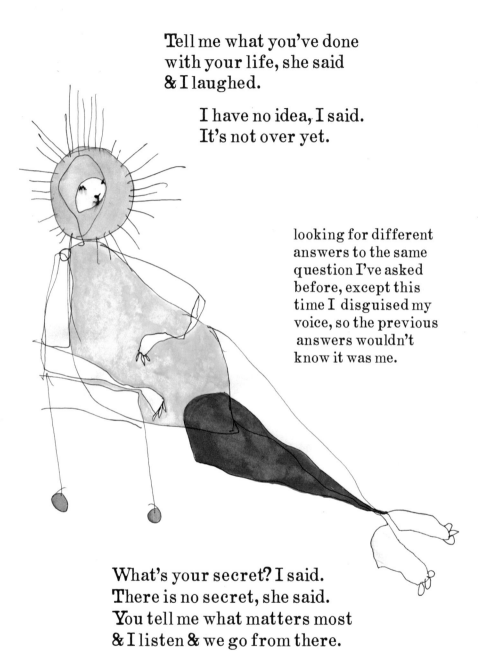

Tell me what you've done
with your life, she said
& I laughed.

I have no idea, I said.
It's not over yet.

looking for different
answers to the same
question I've asked
before, except this
time I disguised my
voice, so the previous
answers wouldn't
know it was me.

What's your secret? I said.
There is no secret, she said.
You tell me what matters most
& I listen & we go from there.

Now & then, you'll
meet your past
unexpectedly
& usually,
it's pretty clear
why you kept going
& left it right
where it was.

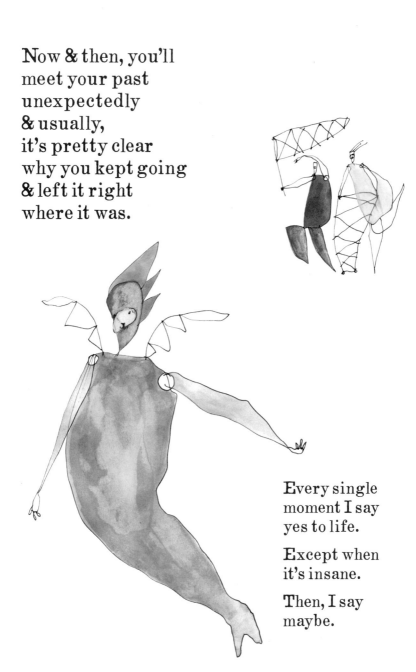

Every single
moment I say
yes to life.

Except when
it's insane.

Then, I say
maybe.

# How Things Work in an Ideal World:

1. Breathe deeply.

2. Laugh fully.

3. Eat good food slowly.

# How Things Work in the Real World:

1. Hold your breath the whole time you're powering through your list of things to do.

2. Smile distractedly. Treat it like the interruption it is. Go back to not breathing.

3. Eat whatever is around really fast, then go back to not breathing.

4. Not breathing is the key. It's the only thing keeping it all together.

Nothing is ever missing.
It's just missing in the
places you expect it to be
& you forget you could go
look for it somewhere else.

completely
convinced that
everything's
turning out fine,
even if fine is
open wildly to
interpretation

It's easy to forget the work just
needs to be done & it doesn't really
care if you don't think you're ready.

It's so easy to miss
how often the world
gives you quiet,
gorgeous moments
& whispers, This is
something I thought
you would love.

Someone asked me today how
you know you're going in the
right direction & I said, You
don't. All you know is if you
feel more alive. If you don't,
you're going in the wrong
direction.

My grandmother used to take us to church with her & when it came time to sing, she always leaned over & whispered, Go ahead & make up your own words, so we did. We were always some of the best singers in that whole church.

One time, the pastor came over for a visit. My grandma brought out butter cookies & coffee & they talked for a long time. I don't remember what he said, but I'll never forget what she said.

Who cares about the words? God just wants to hear you singing.

you are always the light you see by & if
it is dark in the places you look it is only
because you still pretend the light will
have to come from someone else.

what if Love is simply what
you do, like breathing?

& all the places it's hard are reminding
you that sometime in the past, this is
where you forgot to breathe.

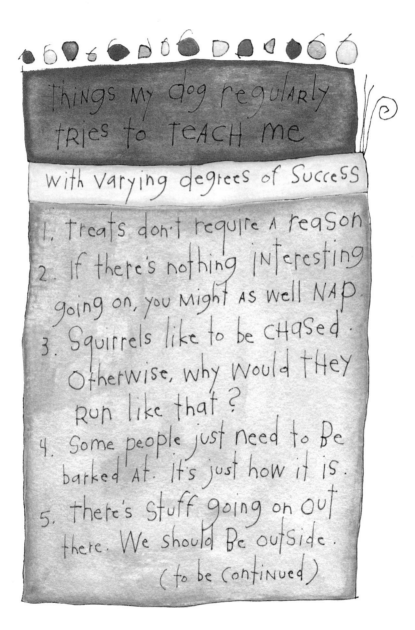

# things my dog regularly tries to TEACH me

## with varying degrees of Success

1. treats don't require a reason
2. If there's nothing interesting going on, you might as well NAP.
3. Squirrels like to be chased. Otherwise, why would they run like that?
4. Some people just need to be barked at. It's just how it is.
5. there's stuff going on out there. We should be outside.

(to be continued)

49

Practicing being royalty for when
everyone around her finally comes
to their senses & sees that she's the
obvious choice for who should run
things.

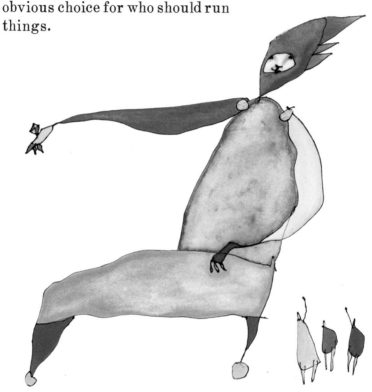

My favorite gift I ever got from
my mom was the gift of laughter
in the face of a serious world & if
I ever had to do it all over again,
I'd definitely ask her for
the same thing.

It may look like nothing's happening
here, other than everyone who comes
near her feels like some of the weight
they've carried their whole lives
suddenly lifts enough for them to
wonder if maybe they've carried
that long enough.

you really have no idea
how it's going to go,
so you might as well
just set out & see for
yourself what shows up.

a little bloated from too
much brewer's yeast, so
she's just going to skitter
around on the surface like a
giant water bug for awhile

right at that fine line between
being willing to leap & being
willing to just walk away & get
a mint chip ice cream cone

The wind never stops here, I said & she said, You must
be new here if you think there is only one wind & not
a hundred different winds, each with their own name
& each entirely different. Later, I wondered how I
could've missed there was more than one wind to do all
that winds must do. Which is why lately you'll often
find me outside, face lifted to the particular wind that
is passing by, whispering, I'm pleased to meet you & if
it's not the first time & I've forgotten, well, I'm pleased
to meet you again.

They only see what they want to
see, I said. It drives me crazy.
My grandmother smiled & nodded.
I hate when people think what
they see is true, she said

& now, even after all
this time, it's still
why I want to be
her when I
grow up.

THIS WAY
to A Clearly
MArKed PAtH
tHAt NO ONE
BuT You HAS ever
WALKed beFore

She read once that life
was precarious & for
a very long time after
that, acted like it was
true.

I know a mermaid who lives in a white
house far from the sea & I watch her
sometimes when she's distracted by
the wind, or the sound of the rain &
I see her eyes glisten as she feels the
pull of wild things that live
in us all.

I wish in that moment we could
all feel how much love there is
in a mermaid's heart because
I think we'd sink to our knees
& thank all that is holy for
her beloved world.

Don't rush to fill your
moments with a song you
already know because each
moment has its own song &
it isn't always something
you've heard before.

In my dream, I was in my grandma's kitchen & she said, What have you done to deserve joy? & I couldn't come up with anything & she laughed & said, Let this be a lesson to you & then she gave me a cookie that tasted like salt air & warm sunlight & the quiet you feel when you sit next to the one you love & then I woke up & the first thing I remember thinking was I need to ask for that recipe.

one of those days I choose to simply be a part of the world that walks around whispering to the other parts about how beautiful they all are

One of the things
I love best is how
much laughter we
find together no
matter which
direction we go.

deciding on her next move
& this is usually where she
remembers she could put it
anywhere in the whole world

if she didn't care about
following all the rules
people are used to.

I had a dream last night where I wasn't exactly the hero,
but I was more like the one everyone turned
to at a critical moment & said What should we do?

I saw the way no one was smiling, so I said,
Dance Break & everyone started dancing &
pretty soon, they started laughing, too & it was
clear the only reason it was critical in the first
place was because everyone got too serious

& the first thing I thought when
I woke up is that there are very
good reasons I'm not in charge of
things like the space program or
national defense.

Feeling like this'd be a perfect
time for a powerful incantation
that would change the entire world
as we know it, but she grew up
watching Disney, so all she
knows is 'Bibbety Bobbety Boo'
& even she doesn't think
that's going to be enough.

(you can't actually see the
sparks except in her head)

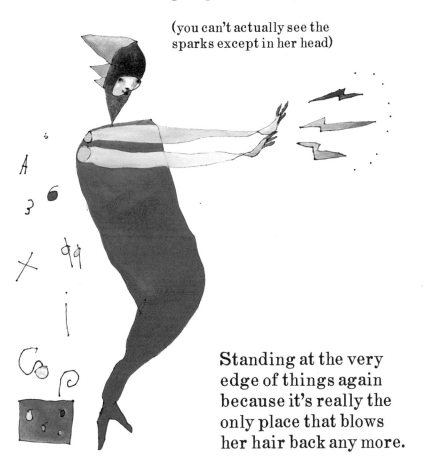

Standing at the very
edge of things again
because it's really the
only place that blows
her hair back any more.

there's a space in her
where the wind blows
through & if you think
how sad you'd miss
that this is always
what happens when
you finally love a
place enough to let it
move through you

A mermaid knows the hardest
thing is going through the days
on land when your heart hears
only the songs of the sea.

Sometimes, you just
need to hear that you're
enough.

Which doesn't mean
that sometimes you
don't also need to hear,
Yeah, you could be better.

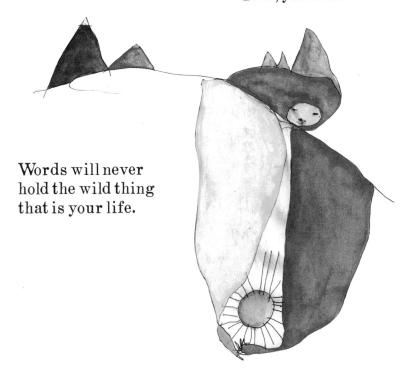

Words will never
hold the wild thing
that is your life.

Love the things you love
with all your heart, so
later on you'll know how
it feels when it comes time
to love the things you
think you don't.

A short Refresher on the WHOLE gratitude thing. in five easy Steps

1. Pick Someone you know.

2. Stop everything you're doing & Really look at them.

3. Tell them why they make your heart melt. Try to use Actual Concrete examples, Sort of like this:
i love the way your Whole fAce lights up When something makes you lAugh unexpectedly OR How you get about TEN feet TALL & lightning Sparks around your HaiR when Someone isn't treated With Love & care & respect.
OR that Way you Come over now & then & sit beside Me & hold my hand & SAY. this is My FaVorite part.

4. give them a hug & Send them Back out into the World. Pick Someone else. Do all of this agAin With them.

5. Later, after a dAy that glows more than usual, Wonder why you don't do this More often

The first & biggest step
is believing the life you
want is possible.

When she was young, people would ask What
have you seen today? & she'd tell them all the
true things, like listening to the wind & feeling
smooth river stones dream of things that only
stones can know & the people would smile as if to
say how imaginative she was, missing entirely
that this is actually how this world is.

Someone asked me how I could be
happy in a world like this &
all I could do was say Because
I don't forget how beautiful
a world can be when you love
it all up.

I don't pay a whole lot of
attention to my birthday,
she said, but don't let
that stop any of you from
putting in some real effort.

Every moment here is
the chance of a lifetime.

A day filled with finding stones
that are shiny with magic & even
if no one else ever believes, it's
one of those things she loves best
about this world.

Convinced the real reason we
evolved to walk upright was so
we'd be able to pick up more rocks.

Fire Goddess on call for Easter
(& you can tell because all the
eggs taste a little smokey & the
chocolate is melted)

It's also why the
Easter Bunny
almost never
calls in sick.

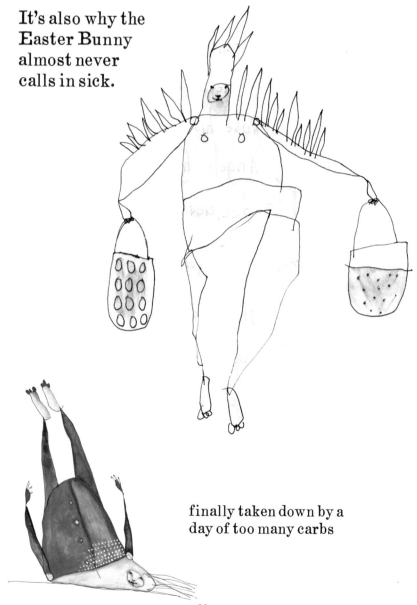

finally taken down by a
day of too many carbs

We walked together on the beach that day
hoping to find some treasure from the sea
& the thing I remember best is laughing at
how everything we found we threw back
so someone else could find it , because we
already had all the treasure we could hold.

it has always been this way from the moment
we met, that even if the whole world said no,
there was nothing that could stand in the way
of hearts who were here to say yes.

When I was growing up one of my mom's
friends was named Joy & she was always
yelling at us to stay away from her flowers
& another woman was named Charity &
every Halloween she'd hand out a single
butterscotch candy in a yellow wrapper
& I think they're how I figured out that
words have nothing to do with what's real.

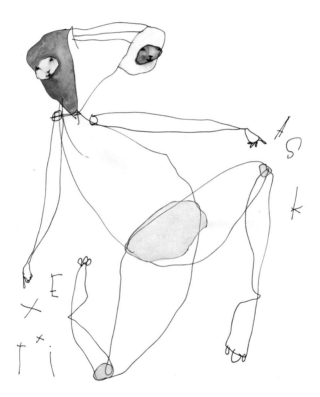

now & then, simply buys a bag of frozen
kale & throws it on the compost pile
because it's easier than pretending
she actually likes it

The thing I've learned about practicing to fly
is there's always a point where you fly or you
don't & after that you practice the other stuff
that comes next, like landing.

This is an invitation to
a whole new world, the
angel said, & I asked if
that meant I had to
change my shirt & the
way she laughed made
me think that'd probably
be the least of it.

There's really not a difficult thing
unless you decide it's a difficult thing.
Otherwise, it's just the next thing
you're figuring out.

When I was ten, I went to the zoo with my class &
all the wild things were in cages & someone asked
why & our teacher said it was to keep them safe &
inside of me, my wild thing growled softly & said,
You cage the things you fear.

& I remember smiling & thinking, We are going
to have an interesting life.

Your heart doesn't ache
because the world could
love better.

It aches because
you could.

People who don't hear living things
whispering all around them are probably
the last people you should listen to about
what's crazy

sometimes the day is
as simple as holding
your hand, glad to be
there for whatever
comes next.

Everything you think you know dissolves pretty fast when you start seeing that there's nothing to know & everything to experience.

Really, knowing anything only matters long enough to know the next thing & the thing after that & so on & so forth. All the real stuff you're going to run into, nobody knows for sure anyway.

THis iS a Box filled with every-thing i KnoW About LiFe (Which Would Be greAt, if it made SeNSe, But it doesn't BecAuSe i didN't PAcK it in there All at the Same tiMe)

In my dream, the angel said
Give up your attachments
& I said, They're the only
thing keeping me here

&the angel leaned over
& whispered, Maybe
here is not where you're
supposed to be
any more.

I used to tell a friend of mine
about all the angels I see &
she'd shake her head & say, I
think you see angels where
there are only people & after
awhile, I stopped saying
anything because her angel
told me that the people part
of her wasn't quite ready
to hear that.

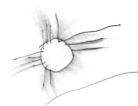

That first morning after,
when the world still tastes
of smoke & ash & grief,
you'll notice the way
the light is different
& only later will you
understand the light
is always different when
you're left with the only
things that matter &
there's nothing standing
between you & that.

It's not that Life doesn't
make any sense. It's just
that Life doesn't always
make sense in the way
you were expecting.

74

# HOW to tell if AN IDEA is GOOD oR BAD.

No. 1 : You get up every morning & you cherish your Self & the People Around you with the tHings you think & say & do. This is a GOOD idea.

No. 2. You get up eVERY morning & mAke the people Around you Miserable & afraid & unSure of theMSelves & you tell yourself it is for their own good. This is A BaD idea.

No. 3 : See how Simple that is?

No. 4 : that is ALL.

When you drag your past
along with you, don't be
surprised if a lot of
people you meet decide
you don't have room
for anything new.

doesn't really believe in magic beans, but checks
them all now & then in case she turns out to be
completely wrong

I started a new practice lately where, instead of celebrating all the times I'm right, I wildly celebrate all the times I'm wrong.

Almost immediately, I noticed two things:

    **1.** it's pretty easy to celebrate continuously &

    **2.** it turns out it's way more fun with everyone joining in, because they like to point out where you're wrong, too

There was one Sunday I remember all the
adults arguing about original sin & since
most of them were my relatives I already
knew they sinned pretty much like everyone
else & if you wanted truly original, what
about Danny O'Reilly stuffing a really
wet poop in a 7-Up bottle & selling it to the
neighbors as special worm food for $5?

Be serious if you must,
but nothing good comes
from forgetting
the best parts
of you are
light.

throwing
invisible
glitter
everywhere
she goes,
because
real glitter
is such a pain
to clean up
afterwards.

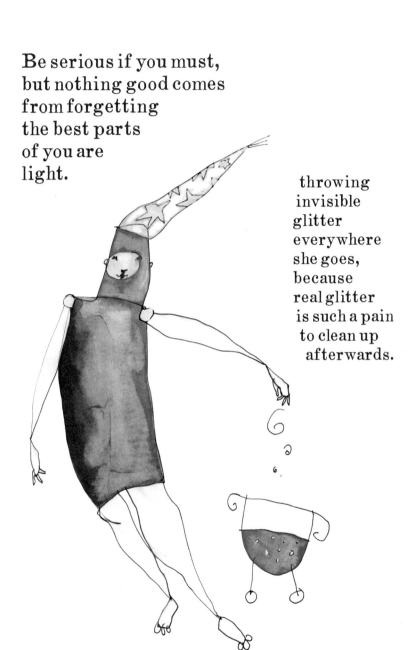

# Two Ways to Live

One way:

1. Imagine a life filled with joy.
2. Continue your usual life until you figure out how you can do that other life.
3. Go on for years & years this way.
4. On your deathbed, wonder what that other life would've been like.

Another way:

1. Imagine a life filled with joy.
2. Go & do it.

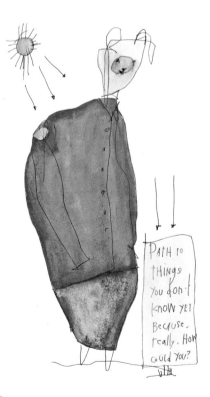

PATH TO THINGS you don't KNOW YET BECAUSE, really, HOW COULD YOU?

Let's say you want a different future &
let's say you want to keep doing things
the same way & let's say I'm a friend of
yours, so I'm going to tell you the truth
about How. Stupid. That. Is. & let's say
you actually listen this time.

(Guess what? That's how you
start to get a different future.)

I had a dream where I was walking down the street
& I could see the heart of everyone I passed & it was
the most beautiful play of light & shadow I'd ever seen
& I completely forgot what brought me here to this
place. Finally, I just stopped walking & everyone
stopped at the same time, too & gathered around me.

It was like being in the middle of an ancient forest,
the light dancing through the leaves on the ground.
Or that moment right at sunrise, when the light
washes over the whole world in an instant.

Someone said, How can we help? I shook my head &
said, Why would you do that? Someone else said, You
would do the same for us. I looked at every one of them
standing there, quietly waiting & suddenly, I knew
what had brought me to this place.

This was the thing I forgot.

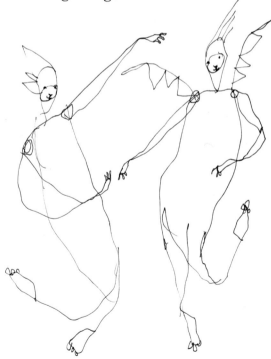

Your life will
be filled with
remarkable
leaps.

A lot of which
will look like
simply
stopping
to see what's
in front of you.

Who you are is the space between darkness
& light & it's always been yours to choose
what you will make with that.

waking early
this morning
to her life
singing strong
& clear,
Come along
with me & see
who we will
become this
day.

There is a thing that goes between people,
a current of light & that is what weaves us
together & our words float on top of that.

This is not something you have to believe.
It is like the sun. Or rain. Or the sound of
birds. Your belief isn't required for those
things to be true all on their own.

This is something to notice & later,
something to practice.

Words are never important by themselves.
They are the light singing through
you & me together.

& if you wonder why you laugh so much
more once you know this, it is because
joy works best at the speed of light.

When people first
invented zero, it was a
leap of faith. Because
while it's easy to count
things, it's not as easy
to count no things.

You might think zero
is nothing. It's not.
Zero is the biggest
number there is.
Because it is all
of the not things.

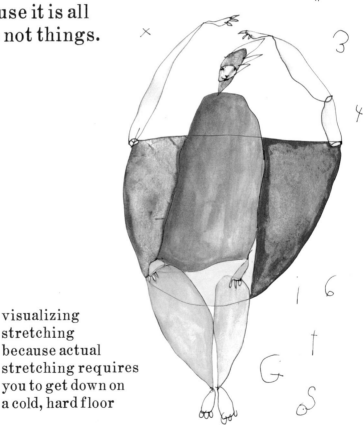

visualizing
stretching
because actual
stretching requires
you to get down on
a cold, hard floor

Something about sitting
here quietly with my coffee
& the hum of people

that makes it clear
there's nowhere else
I need to be.

there are only one or two things that are
truly important & you'll live differently
the moment you choose them,

even if the whole rest of the world
thinks you're wrong.

I used to walk sometimes through the fields on winter nights with my grandfather. Often we'd stop on the ridge where you couldn't see the light from any other houses. We'd stand there quietly together in the snow & starlight.

Every night has its own kind of light, he said one time. You just have to be quiet enough to see it.

& it wasn't until much later that I understood how many dark nights you can walk alone to give someone else that kind of light to see by.

When I was born, I came
with a wild heart, so no one
could ever take the feel of
the wind on my naked skin,
or the voices of the rocks &
trees & other wild things
who were parted from me
at birth.

When I was born, I came
with a wild heart, so no
one could ever make me
forget how to love.

There are always excuses
to be small & afraid, but
don't think it's only a
coincidence that you
already know that's not
the kind of life you're
here to do.

# A Short Guide on How to Listen

1. First breathe. In. Then out. Until you can hear the sound air makes when it fills your lungs.

2. Now, be quieter & quieter until you feel each heartbeat. Quieter even than that so you hear blood as it moves through you.

3. At last, you're quiet enough to listen.

4. If words come up, let them. See them for what they are: things you ask the world to wear to cover its nakedness.

5. The more you listen to the silence in everything, the more you understand. Until at last, with no effort at all, you understand there is never anything to fear & there never was.

Now you know how to listen.

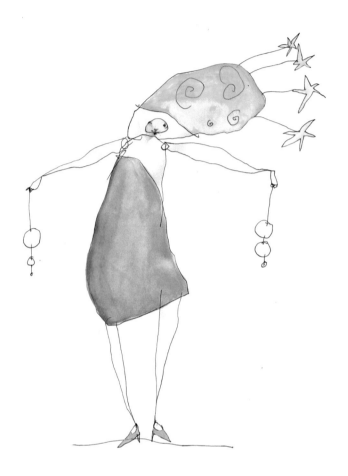

We made up a holiday especially for this
year where you get to believe anything
you want. Only you have to put that in the
basket at the door & then you come inside &
everyone is just happy to be alive together.

& to tell you the truth, I'm wondering who's
going to end up standing outside being mad
at everyone inside being happy together
because they aren't willing to let go of what
they believe, even for a day.

even when they're a thousand miles
apart, not a night goes by where they
don't look up & thank the universe for
the starlight of each other.

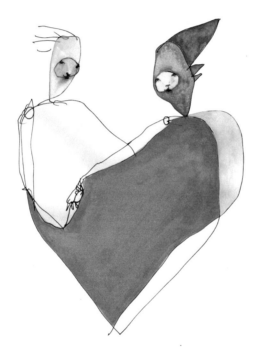

There are moments
throughout our days
when there are no words.
Not because there's nothing more to say,
but because there's so much right here
with us that there are not words enough.

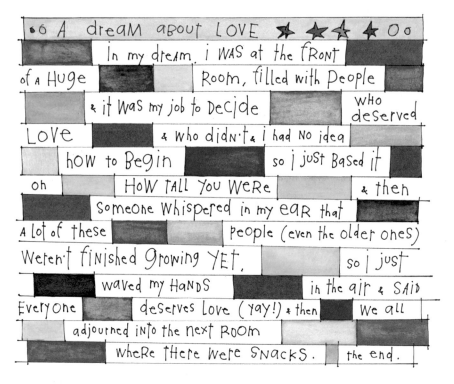

∙₀ A dream about LOVE ★ ★★ ★ ○₀

In my dream, i WAS at the fRont of a HUge Room, filled with people & it Was my job to DeCide who deserved LOVE & who didN't & i had No idea hOW to Begin so i just Based it oh HoW tALL You WeRe & then someone Whispered in my eaR that A lot of these people (even the older ones) Weren't fiNished growing YET. so i just waved my HaNDS in the air & SAiD EveryOne deserves Love (yay!) & then We all adjourned into the next Room wheRe tHere Were SNackS. the end.

92

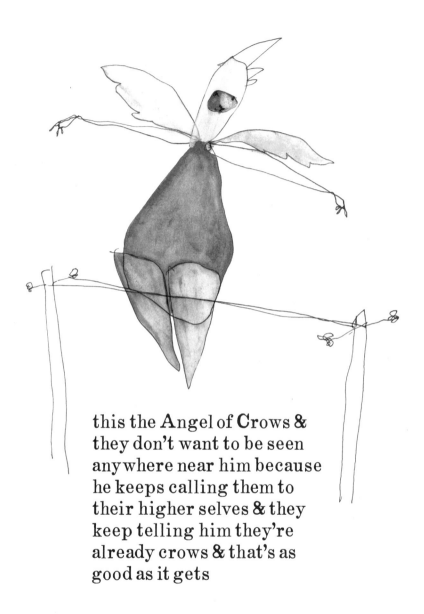

this the Angel of Crows &
they don't want to be seen
anywhere near him because
he keeps calling them to
their higher selves & they
keep telling him they're
already crows & that's as
good as it gets

This is filled with all the
perfect words you need to
hear at this exact moment in
your life & you'll be amazed
at how they seem familiar, as
if you've read them before in
passing, or overheard them
in a restaurant, or coffee
shop.

I'll tell you a secret: they're
the same words as before,
only now you're willing
to believe they could be
for you.

& if these are not the words
you're expecting, just
know this: the words you
need are still right here,

but you may have to
close your eyes to listen,
without the distraction
of what you think
you're reading.

You can make love fit into any shape you want, my aunt once told me. Just make sure that it's a shape that holds you, too.

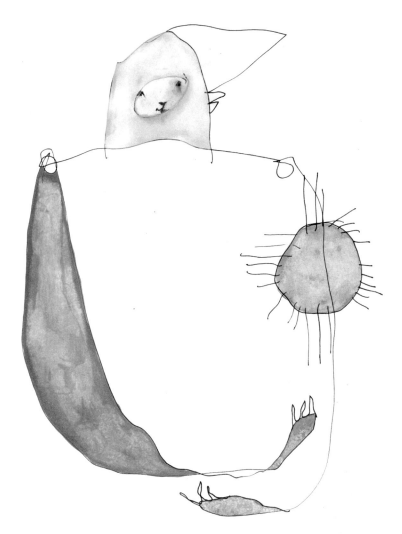

I forget how quiet it must have been all that time you loved alone.

I breathe you in &
there it is again, my
heart saying thank
you for this whole life
that brought me here
to you.

The night was
so full of quiet
there was nothing
either of us
needed to add

It's not easy to
explain until it
happens, that
moment when
your eyes meet
& suddenly,
your heart
has a whole
new future.

A lot of people will do the same
thing over & over again even when
it's not working because a new thing
is hard & if they get it wrong, people
might laugh, but then I remember
everyone dies anyway

& what's your reason again for not
trying something new when the old
thing isn't working?

Every single
one of us needs
every single
one of us.

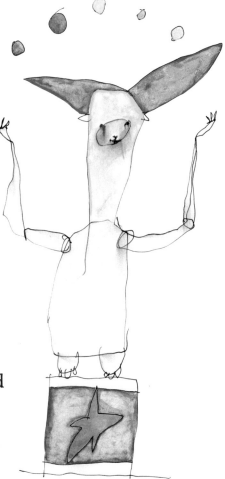

It's easy to see
the attraction
of the future,
since everyone
there hasn't
already decided
who they think
you are yet.

THRee things to ReMember
At the Start of Every day

#1. This is your Real LiFe.

#2. Joy is easier to See
when you quit Complaining.

#3. You Never Know WHAT
the THIRd thing is going to
Be until later, so try to
Pay AttenTion
so you don't Miss it.

When I was ten, my grandmother discovered knitting &
that Christmas, she gave all of us kids tube sweaters in
odd colors she got on sale at the discount yarn store. I'd
never heard of a tube sweater & I asked my mom about it.
She invented it all on her own, my mom said, because she
isn't very good at knitting yet. You only have to wear it
when she visits, she added. Just try not to fall over
because you'll probably hurt something.

(My mother grew up with my grandmother, so she had
a lot of experience with this kind of thing.)

I was reading last night about thin places where magic is near enough to touch & I wondered if I'd ever been near one & right then you sat next to me & pointed through the bare trees at the new moon rising & the sky was blue & dark & there you were, warm beside me & maybe the real thin places are the moments you let yourself fall away enough to see.

This world is no real home
without all of us here.

Looking for a place to plant her
dreams & after all this time,
she sees that right where she is
might be the perfect spot.

How does it change the movement of your
days when you see everything you do with
this life is a way to say thank you?

It can take some time
to understand that
stillness is not no
movement.

It is movement
at exactly the
speed of now.

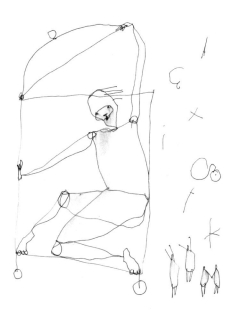

Transparency has
nothing to do with
telling everybody
everything. It's how
you begin to see who
you are, so you can be
better at heading
towards who you
want to be.

she stood there waiting to see what
the sea would bring & the sea brought
everything she imagined: grief &
sadness & laughter & wonder,
because the sea brought her
only itself & met her exactly
where she was

knows that scattering
bread crumbs works
for goldfish, so she's
hoping a high-quality
gluten-free muffin will
pull in a mermaid or two

Not particularly concerned with what people
think about her as long as she's fine with the
things she ends up thinking about herself.

This is a special birthday story that's been around for almost your whole life, so it sparkles a lot more than most other stories, because it's been watching you grow into you & there's not a lot more sparklier anything than that.

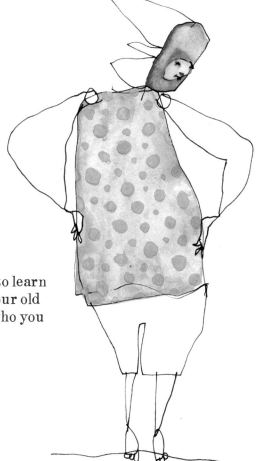

convinced that polka dots have much to teach us, but not many are willing to pay the price to learn

It's a big thing to learn you don't owe your old self any say in who you want to be now.

The mistake you might make at first is believing
the wind cares at all what people think. First, you
listen to the wind & later on, if you're lucky, you
come to see it's always only been singing of the joy
of being exactly who it is & if that's a good thing
for people to hear, the wind is fine with that.

Incantation for this day:
Oh that this day be filled
with the usual things &
if only for a moment with
each one, I stop in their
presence & listen & wonder
how I ever missed this
particular song, so
beautiful & rich &
strange.

THRONe
OF KNOWING
EVERYTHING

When we go out walking,
sometimes we face the wind
& sometimes it's at our backs &
never once have we given up
in despair because the wind
did not agree with where we
wanted to go.

**Not quite sure which
of my life choices have
led to snow, but quite
sure that next year
there are definitely
going to be different
choices**

not sure if you can call it roughing it when
all it is is forgetting to close the bedroom
window last night

Last night, I walked in the cold & there was no other sound but the crunch of my boots on snow & then, almost too soft to hear, there was the thin crystal song of starlight & I stopped & listened for a long time & somewhere in there, the universe suddenly made sense. But by the time I got home, it didn't any more. Still, it made me smile at how little that mattered now I'd heard the starlight sing.

There are parts of life that are like a
door into nothing you've ever known
& when you come back, you close it
quietly & with wide eyes, whisper to
anyone who wants to know, you'll just
have to see for yourself.

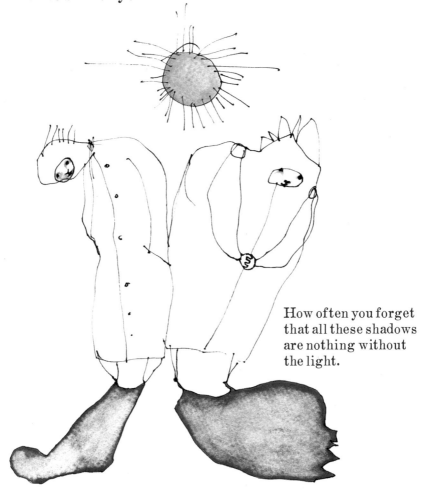

How often you forget
that all these shadows
are nothing without
the light.

What if your shame
is not the thing
that happened?

What if
it's that
you weren't
considered
important
enough
for that to
matter?

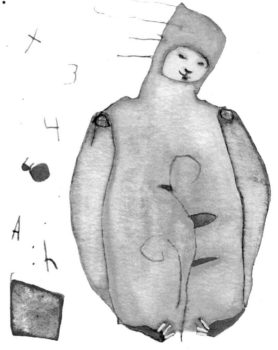

It is not mine to decide
how long you take to
grieve the life stolen
from you.

Sometimes, the real sadness comes
when you ask yourself why you
ignore your own heart for so long?

In my dream, a couple of angels & I were sitting quietly on a bench, looking at the sky. Why didn't you tell me I was going the wrong way? I said. They shrugged & said, We did, but you were more interested in going that other way for awhile & the thing is it's hard to stay angry at your angels for too long when it's your own damn fault.

The stories that sing to your heart are never really about the world. They're about who you want to be.

Sitting there quietly
amazed at how easily
the sounds of a hundred
ordinary conversations
turn into a single song
of love

You'd probably be
surprised how many
angels I meet who tell
me to keep it to myself
since they finally got us
all to the point where
we're thinking we
might as well get to
work because this
heaven-on-earth stuff
isn't going to do itself.

convinced this morning that
evolution would never have
happened without coffee.

today's happy dance
is twice as high off
the ground as usual
because she's got
twice as many things
she's decided to be
happy about

All set this morning to give a big speech
about how birthdays are no big deal, but then
she saw all the presents & she decided she
didn't have the heart to crush all that fun.

the first ones to map the
stars also knew to map the
dark places in between,
because they saw the world
as it was, whole & alive
& every path you take is
never only one thing but
always threading between
the known & the unknown,
between where you are
going & what you
imagine that
to be.

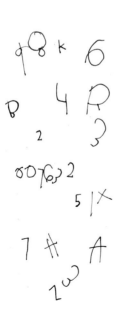

There are no secrets here.
Only things you haven't
remembered. Yet.

## about brian

Brian Andreas is the pen name of artist & writer Kai Skye,
known around the world for his lyrical work celebrating the
strength, beauty & boundless possibility of the human spirit.
This is his fifteenth book, filled with the colorful drawings
& short stories that have accompanied so many of you
through the quiet moments of your own lives.

After 25 years of balancing artmaking with running a
company, he's now going in a whole new direction. Working
daily in the studio, side by side with Fia. Making beautiful
things with their hands. Writing. Drawing. Listening to hear
what two people can create in the world together.

## about flying edna

flying edna is a small company. Two artists & a dog.
Everything we write, create, & teach is about experiencing
interconnectedness & cultivating the practice of presence.
It's about going towards a life you love. Which is why, in our
own studio, we choose environmentally conscious practices
& work with sustainable materials we find from fellow
makers & vendors who share our respect for the planet.

Since meeting in 2015, Fia, Brian and Yoshi have journeyed
together through 45 states, temporarily making their home
in the Midwest, Maine, and most recently Montana. By the
time you read this, they may be off on another journey, but
you can always find them at www.flyingedna.com

flying edna